To always remember our years
in Dubai for my family,
Gerhard, Rebecca, Alexander and Ricarda

Ebenwald Verlag

Wattens, Austria

www.Camel-O-Shy.com

ISBN: 3-902515-00-7

First publshed in 2003 by Magrudy's, Dubai, UAE

Reprint 2005

Printed in China

A WEEK WITH CAMEL-O-SHY

This book belongs to

Alanah Sherwood

4

There lives a camel in the desert of Dubai ...
the camel's name is Camel-O-Shy.
And do you know why?
Because this camel is so shy.

Can you see the tiny speck in the desert?
Is it Camel-O-Shy?

Have a look through these binoculars!

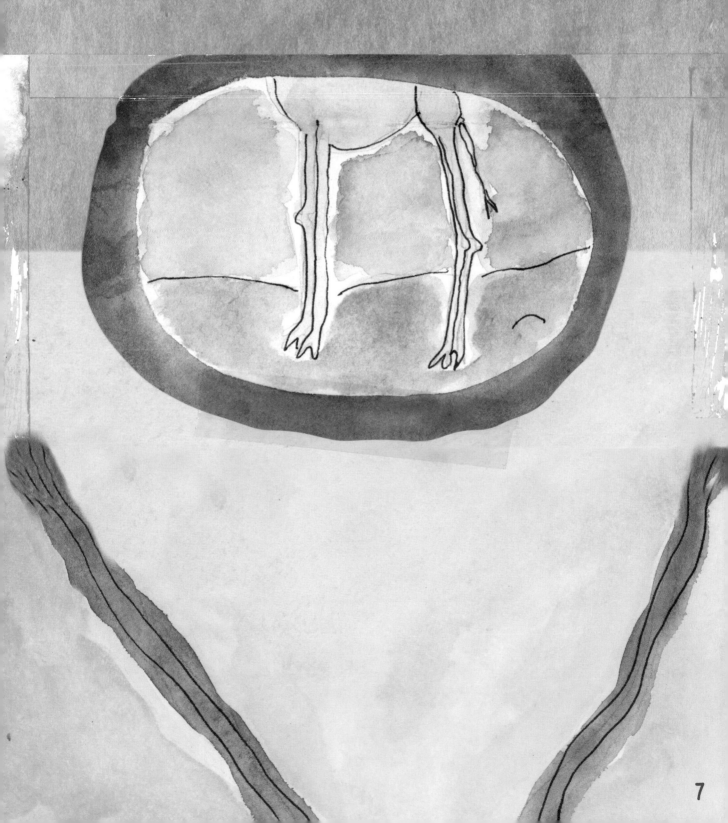

Camel-O-Shy! Here is a letter for you!

PLEASE OPEN IT AND TELL ME WHAT'S
WRITTEN INSIDE?